Cub and Pua

by Liza Charlesworth

ISBN: 978-1-338-84422-1

Art Director: Tannaz Fassihi; Designer: Cynthia Ng; Illustrated by Kevin Zimmer
Copyright © Liza Charlesworth. All rights reserved. Published by Scholastic Inc.

3 4 5 6 7 68 26 25 24

Printed in Jiaxing, China. First printing, June 2022.

■SCHOLASTIC

It is Cub!
It is his pal, Pug!

2

Cub and Pug
sit in the sun.
It is hot.

3

Then Cub and Pug
run and hop...

in the mud.
Mud, mud!

Cub and Pug dig
in the mud.
Mud, mud!

Cub and Pug tug
in the mud.
Mud, mud!

6

Cub and Pug hug
in the mud.
Mud, mud!

Mud on Cub!
Mud on Pug!
Mud is fun.
But mud is YUCK!

Then Cub and Pug run
and hop...

in a tub.
It is hot.

Cub and Pug
dump in a big, big
jug of suds.

A lot of suds on Cub!
A lot of suds on Pug!

A hot tub of suds
is as fun as mud!

Read & Review

Invite your learner to point to each short-*u* word and read it aloud.

tug

cub

pug

fun

hug

run

suds

15

Fun Fill-Ins

Read the sentences aloud, inviting your learner to complete them using the short-*u* words in the box.

> Pug   tub   sun   mud   fun

1. Cub's pal is _____.

2. First, Cub and Pug sit in the _____.

3. Then, Cub and Pug get messy in the _____.

4. After that, Cub and Pug get clean in the _____.

5. A hot tub of suds is _____!